Special thanks to the team who helped create this book:
Editor: Bianka Walter and Illustrator: Mohamed Daamouche

Written by E.K. Finlay
ISBN Paperback: 978-1-9168743-0-5
First edition 2021
www.ekfinlay.com

WHAT BROCCOLI DON'T LIKE

E.K. FINLAY

Why is it you don't like us?
We're really very yummy,
And if you actually tried us,
You'd have a happy tummy!

Being **green** is very cool,

And amazing, you'll agree.

We're actually a superfood,

And look just like a **tree!**

It's really quite upsetting,
To be left, last on your plate,
You don't know what you're missing,
So, I'll tell you what WE hate!

Hotdogs are the problem,

They really are so bad,

We wish they could be awesome,

But instead, they make us sad!

We all know **green** is healthy,
Red and **orange** as well, it's true,
But none of you can tell me,
That **brown** is good for you!

We sometimes wonder why it is ,
You choose the things you do?
Picking **hotdog** instead of **broccoli**,
When we also taste good too!

If a broccoli raced a **hotdog**,
I know who'd win for sure,
We'd be running speedy,
As we're healthy, green
and pure.

So how would you do in a race,
Depending on who you ate?
With us, your legs are flying,
With a **hotdog**, you'll be late!

Broccoli can swim as well,
And sausage can, it's true,
But can you tell what happens,
To a bun with no canoe?

Eat us when you go **swimming**,
You'll be a **superstar**,
If not, we'll go fishing,
Before you sink too far!

If broccoli goes bouncing,
We always have such fun,
Soaring up through the sky,
Much higher than a bun!

Imagine if you ate us,
Just think what you could be.
A supersonic meteor,
Zooming high and flying free!

Being green is helpful,
Especially playing games.
Who is the easiest to spot?
I won't mention any names!

So maybe that's the reason,
Why we get left on the side,
And children cannot see us,
Is it how good we hide?

One project you could try,

Is to plant some **broccoli**.

Just add a little water,

And grow your own small **tree**.

Broccoli is so useful,
I'm sure that you can see,
From salads, soup or roasted,
Great choices, you'll agree!

But a **hotdog** in your hand,
Is really nothing new,
Are there any other recipes?
Could you put them in a stew?

So if you're still not sure,
Please follow this little plan,
On how to zing up how we taste,
Go on, you know you can!

Just pour a splash of **ketchup**,
We have a handy trunk,
Now go ahead and grab on tight,
And have a little dunk!

YIPPEE!

Another trick that we can do,

Whiz us up and in a flash,

We can turn potato,

Into **SCARY ZOMBIE MASH!**

WHOOSH!

What else could we turn **green**?
Maybe we could try **ice-cream**?
Don't know if that would work,
But it sure is fun to dream.

Now we shouldn't be unfair,
Having a choice is the key,
So maybe there is a way,
For hotdogs AND broccoli

Together on the plate,
What a combo we could be,
A hotdog for the fun stuff,
And us to keep you so healthy!

Or could we get creative,
To set our taste buds free,
And put the two together,
A broc-dog we would be!

So maybe I should think again,
It's really bad to hate,
I truly love my **hotdog** buddy,
He is my bestest mate!

Broccoli Activity Pack

Thank you so much for buying this book, I hope you enjoy reading it as much as I enjoyed writing it.

As a thank you, I would like to send you my Broccoli Activity Pack with all this free stuff:

1. A free audio version of the book for your children to follow along with as they read the book.

2. Colouring worksheets featuring images from the book for children to create their own versions of the story.

3. Puzzles and activities for children to do based on the characters in the book.

4. The Zombie Mash recipe for your children to try and enjoy.

You can get all of this, for free, just go to: https://books.ekfinlay.com/broccoli

Thanks again

Made in United States
North Haven, CT
31 March 2022

17724012R00018